ALIVE AND KICKING

- Stride -

ALIVE AND KICKING

Young Devon Writers
selected by
Rupert M Loydell

ALIVE AND KICKING
First edition 1991
Copyright individual authors
All rights reserved

ISBN 1 873012 20 9

Cover artwork by Steven Williams
Copyright 1991

Published by
STRIDE
37 Portland Street
Newtown, Exeter
Devon EX1 2EG
England

Contents

HORSE

Stable-sleeper, steady-walker,
Noise-maker, hay-muncher,
High-jumper, sugar-beet eater,
Brown-eyed beauty.
Fast-mover, apple-cruncher,
Slow-stalker, carrot-swallower,
My horse is beautiful.

James Bagwell

THE GIRL IN THE PICTURE

I stood there looking for her
Gran was there by the light of the oil lamp that lit the dark room
I heard a noise,
A quiet still noise of footsteps.
I though to myself "It must be her, it must".
"Oh, come on, Mum", I say to myself.
A dark friendly shadow walks along.
I can see it on the wall.
"Mum", I say to myself, "It must be her".
It was.
I ran out and hugged her.

Judith Allnutt

THE HOT STILL

It's hot and teapots are rattling,
God I wish I was home
Cups are clashing
Frying tomatoes again

I wanted money in my pocket
Any my legs are getting tired
Cutlery Rattling
Water Rushing
There's a noise from the Restaurant

Radio going we're listening to the National
Orders being shouted
Water Bubbling
Teapots knocked
People sucking Coke up straws

Noel Beavis

CONTRACTUAL RELATIONSHIPS

The darkness amplified the sound
Of printer's ink on the marriage contract
Smiling smugly, smothering his soul
Hiding his heart,
Concealing his conscience.

I am the Island - he is the sea.

Heavy, furrowed face, cracking smiles,
The grey, worn boots return again.
Annuled is printed across the contract.
The vases fly,
As do I.

See the Island - it is he.

Propping up the bar, "I'll have another".
Washing his life with vigorous drinking.
The boats have holes in. What else does?
No more wife,
Very little life.

The Island gazes out to sea.

Gareth Bewley

THE CARRIAGE CLOCK

The customary wedding gift has stopped,
No tick.
I sit next to your boots.
No tock.
Grey, worn boots, grey, worn life,
No tick.
The bruises stain on all our minds,
No tock.
Now we all share the power - brain over brawn,
No tick.
"Why don't we remember the children?"
No.
Why don't we remember the children?

The carriage clock falls voluntarily to the brusque
man's grey, worn boots. It doesn't break.
He doesn't blink.
All he does is scowl.

Gareth Bewley

HEROINE

She can't be a heroine.
Her mind is taken and opened to the stars,
Her face is white and her eyes speak
Death.
She awakes before dawn
And shakes the silence from her hair.
Calling her from beyond the edge
Is the immaculate end.

Amy Bickford

THE RUNAWAY

She looks for shelter in the night,
She turns her head when two men fight.
She's grasping her home in a carrier bag,
Her trousers are torn and her coat is a rag.
She's silently suffering and nobody knows,
She's hungry and dirty but high on her toes.
She's sliding through shadows - a fox out of breath,
Her misery's eternal, but a shortcut is death.

Rachel Blackmore

OCEAN SCULPTURE

Salt sharpening my tongue
Smooth faces stop,
Cutting.
I smell the sweat of the sea.
A thousand brown lines
Running
Grain in eternal circles.
Hollows hiding secrets;
Exploring,
My fingers searching
Pebble - beaten wood.
And time

Catherine Boyce

CONSCIOUS ABUSE

I hear it and see it
The bone snaps easily
He doesn't know I'm there
Watching, Waiting

The pain on her face
As her wrist falls limply
Her condescension rising
Humble, Humiliating

He hits her again
She had done nothing wrong
There is no excuse
Disgrace, Debilitating

How can I help her
She needs me now
The screams ring through me
Anguish, Abating

I shout out loud
He whirls around angrily
The face has no emotion
Hard, Hating

He steps towards me
I grab her and run
My heart is in my mouth
Panting, Palpitating

I am running forever
She relaxes and cries
The bruises on her face
Eschew, Equating

The emotion of abuse
Is plain for all to see
I hate him for his actions
Forbidding, Frustrating

Mary Cockman

BATTLE FOR SURVIVAL

As the blossom fell,
Clinging softly to the night,
Echoing the last deserted yell,
Staggering,
Into the illuminated light,
Chiming screams,
Burdened Sunday church bells,
Determination,
Cheating death,
Too proud to die without a fight.

Suzanne Conway

THE FLUENT NIGHT

The roar of the ocean,
The song of the birds,
The poetic motion,
The rhythm of words.

The society at rest,
The silence of the night,
The chicks in their nests,
The brightness of the lights.

"Sssssh" said the man,
As it echoed through the land,
And the beauty of the night,
Shuddered into flight.

Suzanne Conway

A TASTE OF FREEDOM

Open your mind to a new beginning;
One filled with happiness and love,
Desires,
Fire crying in those deserted eyes,
Closed.
Too tender and vulnerable to sight the
indifferent.
The softness of his pale, pure, virgin
skin.
Carpet solemnly untouched, over his
fragile, pounding heart.
Now time has ticked away,
He is ready for eternal life,
However long that may last.

Suzanne Conway

TIGER

Fierce cat, bone-shaker,
Big-eyed and shiny teeth,
Power-pouncer, day-stalker,
Night-walker, eye-catcher,
Blood-letter, heart-stopper,
Home-shaker, meat-eater,
Night-hunter, man-eater.

Nicholas Courtney

SLOPPY KISS

I hadn't been to visit my Great Aunty Bett
for 5 years,
she lives so far away.
As it was her birthday we were going to visit.
When I got there Aunty Bett gave me
A smacking great kiss, as always,

Bluur.

I sat in may favourite paisley chair
and listened to the big old grandfather clock,

Tick Tock Tick Tock

Nothing had changed.

The coal was glowing in the fireplace
So warm and friendly,
Old Tom cat was curled up in his favourite chair
like he hadn't moved since five years.

Aunt brought in the tea with a big slice
of the special flavour chocolate sponge cake,
We drank from the same china set as before.

Nothing had changed at all.

Gavin Davey

THE BOY I LOVE

The boy I like,
likes my best friend ...
The boy I love,
loves my best friend ...
The boy I used to love,
loved my best friend ...
Anyone else love my best friend?

Kati Doubleday

HUMDRUM

I fidget
I scratch
I stare
I'm bored
Humdrum

Kati Doubleday

O THIS NIGHT WAS SO GLIM

This night was so glim
All I could see was the
mirror shining on the wall
Street light shining through
the curtains
All I could smell was
Potato from tea time
Stale cigarette ash.
All I could hear was the
Bus going up the hill
Next door making a rattle

O this night was so glim

David Essam

THE PILLOW

The feathered pillow lies mishaped and used,
covered in a layer of dreams,
Scented with the sweet smell of sleep,
beckoning the weary head,
it's a tired man's refuge.

Becky Forest

THE RIGHT

Stuck in a cage all the rest of your life,
Nothing to conquer, no trouble or strife.
Nowhere to run freely, wild as the storm.
Nothing to do except sit and to mourn.

How can you move in a box so small
I bet you just wish you could play ball,
With the ones who locked you in this tiny space,
Just so they can safely powder their face.

You were roaming the seas a while ago
As alive as the trees in the wind, but no!
Not any more, you're weak and tired
After the shot that was carried,
Loaded and fired.

Stuck in a barn, collapsed on the floor,
Your eyes staring hopefully at the old wooden door.
You're hungry and lonely,
Just made out of bones.
At a movement you sound like an old can of stones.

Who's got the right to lock them up in a cage,
Who's got the right to kill for old age.
Who gave the right to kill and to hunt
Who said OK to the cruel evil stunts.

Rachel Giles

BIRD BRAIN

It's been a while
since my brain leapt out of head in the morning
and flew with the birds
singing about the joy of life,
then hopped down to the gym
to pump some poetry
before jogging home through novel pages
for feeding once again.

Just lately it's become disillusioned, self-pitying even,
preferring to wallow in my cosy sack of mother skin
and wade through leaves
of tabloid papers, munching on TV dinners.
It was once an anarchic, evergreen teenager
protesting, lusting, fecund,
sucking inspiration from the roots of the earth.

These days it's a respectable citizen
operating nine to five only,
bum on chair, in the office,
imagination locked away in the safe,
its once naked, vibrant flesh
concealed in suits,
tailor made,
ties as tight as electric cable
no sparks can escape.

My brain which was once
a hot steak on the world's ice rink,
as raw as eggs, free as the sky,
is now dry like gravestones under the feet,
as numb as ten pence between the teeth.
In fact, it has become as ordinary as the day
is long.

Gemma Green

BOAT SONG

I've seen a ripple on the ice pool
the delicate wave of spiky frost
has cut into a smile

Cupid Bowed

There's a rainbow on the ice rink
laid in the permanent ink
the colours neatly woven

Cupid sowed

I've seen a slit in the plastic mirror
river sharp, razor soft
the boat sailed through

Cupid prowed.

Gemma Green

BUT

You always heard but
You weren't doing the screaming.
You could always see but
You were blind to the pain.
You always felt but
You weren't doing the hurting.
You could always believe but
It wasn't your problem.
You always knew but
It was your skin you were saving.

Amy Griffiths

RED

Red is ... the blood which falls from cut skin
Pumped around by the heart which beats from within
Red is ... the colour on your report
Telling you how much less you got than you thought
Red is ... the pain in closed eyes
Coming from mouths streaming endless lies
Red is ... the colour of the night sky
Delight to all shepherds for tomorrow will be dry
Red is ... the colour of painted mouths
Behind which is kept the screams and the howls

Amy Griffiths

CAGED

Out of the corner of a cosmetic stuck eye.
A stolen rabbit watches,
As a needle is thrust hard into it's hide.
It lets out a silent scream

Bald headed, caged rodents watch their native brother.
Stacked like boxes. Gawking in silent fear.
Waiting, anxiously,
For the unknown pain to strike.

Tanya Haigh

THE POEM OF LOST LOVE

He saw her, yet she didn't speak,
It was her, he was sure.
That same look that meant so much
Made the hurt even more.

She wasn't alone, that was the reason,
Times they'd spent, she'd forgotten,
Basketball games he'd let her win,
In the summer.

But now it's the autumn.

Nicola Haley

TIME

Purple clouds
Pink midnight sky
Open doors
Closed rivers
Running policemen from the crowd
Shouting obcenities
Closing the world

Testing on sniffer dogs
Bleaching the rabbit
Waiting for yesterday
When there was no wheel
Inventing the parliament
Killing the free

Which way would you go
If the wheel was not there
Which way would the globe go
Where would the rivers run
Over the bridges or under the sea
Which way would you go

Spray painted Stonehenge
My red rinse ran out
Run after it
Run after it
As fast as you can

I was the one who took it
You'll never catch me
You can put me in jail
Throw away the key
But my spirit still runs
Away from the police

876 worldwide
numbers, numbers
Why on earth do we need them
They scatter my brain
They deaden my arteries
Waiting for my time to run out
Counting away my twilight years in the pink midnight sky

Juli Harris & Zoe Leworthy

WALKING IN THE MOONLIGHT

Frosty stars
And brilliant moonlight
Cast shadows
From crisply-silhouetted hedgerows.
We walked from the warmth of our home
Towards lonely, clear darkness,
Passing dimly-lit windows of cosy cottages.
Flames danced on the walls,
Leaping, beckoning:
"Take a sip of our hot, soothing chocolate,
It will warm your numbing fingers".
But we continued onwards.
It became apparent
That the glow of our village
Was far behind in the distance.
A strange sense of nothing was in front of us.
We became aware of every movement.
Every noise.
I reached for the security of my daddy's hand,
Through his hand I could almost feel Electric excitement
Of being blinded by night,
Not seeing anything,
Depending on just our ears.
Somehow he didn't need his eyes,
He knew the way.
Suddenly, from nowhere,
Two beams of light reached for the sky,
Grabbing at the stars.
He pulled me into the hedge
As the monster roared past.
Like spies,
We watched them pass,
Deeper into the night.

Alison Hatten

ANIMAL RIGHTS

He came to take us away
He came to capture us and tame the unknown
He came to make fools of us, before our friends.
He came to hurt us and make us ill.

Protect ourselves, fight back.
Protect our instincts of killing and hunting.
Protect our ancestors pride.
Protect our future for all to see.

Should we have to put up with this?
Should we be locked in gloom and doom?
Should we become the hunted?
Should we have our coats worn by others?

Animals have their own kingdom
Animals don't kill humans for their skins
Animals kill for their food and nothing else
Animals have a way of life that no one else will ever change.

Tim Keast

EVOLUTION

Evolution
Is hung in a gallery
Of wire mesh walls,
Concrete floors
And no open doors.
An exhibit,
A species
Each named by a plaque
Reluctantly presenting themselves as an act.
All are starved and immune
Of their land, sea and air
In which their parentage lived ages
But now, they are caged,
To reassure pure existance.
They are protected from man,
And are patronized, exploited,
Stripped of their dignity,
Drained of all will
To live such a life
Of unrecognised supremacy.

And where will they be,
In a thousand years time?
Made extinct by a marvellous, purblind man.

Ruth Kemp

THE VALLEY

The sun rises over a valley of trees,
Where the fresh green leaves hang.
The boughs sway gently in the breeze,
And grass blades silently bang. A mass of
butter cups,
And birds do softly sing,
Sweetly talking like little pups,
As a carpet of bluebells happily ring.
The water rushes over rocks.
Fish ripple as they swim.
Behind a tree creeps a fox,
His shadow darkens as it gets dim.
Not a stir over the hills,
Everything settles; everything's still.

Tanya Kenwood

MANS BEST FRIEND

Cage by cage, dog by dog,
Owners cannot be found
Breed by breed, bark by bark,
The shuddering greyness of the pound.

But once there was a happy time,
When puppy bought, a friend is found
All the memories of Mum were gone
Now just the child with the loving cluster
Of toys to spoil and joy to muster.

Times got hard and puppy forgotten
He was too small, too large, too pricey or too weak,
So put in a pound.
Now friend was enemy.

Amongst his rag and bowl
He seemed to wonder what he'd done
to be mistreated and put in a cage
Like a common thief.
He never seems to laugh or play,
Just sits there without emotions.

But now his time has come,
To leave the pound and cage.
The sharp point is nearly here
A quick goodbye and then ...
A pain behind.

William Klinkenberg

KITES

My kite flys higher than any bird
High in the open sky
Gliding, swooping, ascending,
Flexing, bending, looping.

The wind blows in a gust
That makes my kite hard to trust
Pulling at the elastic frame
Making flying like a game.

Animals look in wonder
At the bird on strings,
How does it fly,
Without flapping its wings?

It hovers in the air,
Like a bird of prey,
In the humid wildness,
In the sky so grey.

Flying kites in farmers' fields,
Wheeling over farmers' yields.

Flying kites on pebbly beaches,
Whilst a sea gull scorns and screaches.

Flying kites on a windy hill,
The wind blowing all it will.

Flying a kite in the sky,
soaring through heavens so high.

In my hands a home-made kite
In my mind a bird so bright.
With wonderous, gracefulness and light.

B. Lewin

A TRIP AROUND THE HARBOUR

Slowly we chug away from the port
The boat is crowded and noisy
I can smell the engine
And feel the waves slap against the side

The sun shines in my eyes
As we swing towards the ships
I can not believe their massive size
As I've only ever seen them on TV

They are grey steel giants
With their flags flying high
And each letter and number
Tells of the job they have done

I feel sad but proud
The shells and guns
Bringing pain and death
To people like you and me

Away from the ships of war
I see the ferries and fishing boats
Busy and bustling
At the end of the day

James Martin

OWL

Night hunter
Gliding between shiny stars.
Swift flier
Circling in the windless air.
Bright eyes searching for
Small creatures.
The mice scarer, mole catcher,
Rat swallower,
Sharpened talons waiting
for an attack.
A loud screech of
Triumph.
Steady beating wings,
Retiring to his battered barn.
Day sleeper resting
While the sun goes by.
Ears buried in soft feathers,
Dark body of shaded brown,
Hooked beak tightly closed.
Metre wide wings
like the wings of an aeroplane.

And when the sun has disappeared,
Another screech of triumph.

Claire Morgan

AUTUMN SEASON

The Autumn season,
No leaves on the trees
There must be a reason,
There's no flowers or bees.

The cloud is cold and grey,
The sun struggles through,
The houses are dark,
Holding people with flu.

The wind starts to howl,
It blows through the streets,
Lifting papers and rubbish,
That entangle your feet.

The rain keeps on falling,
The mist fails to clear,
Days getting colder,
As winter draws near.

Andrew Moss

MAWGAN PORTH

Family days at Mawgan Porth;
The sun beats down on the golden sand,
Away in the distance the surfers
Top the azure-coloured waves.
Swimming and jumping the crashing foam
They ride the breakers till they fall and die.
On the beach with bath towels spread
Shining bodies bake in the heat of the blazing sun,
Contented with the morning's ride.

Now the sands are busy like a nest of ants,
Figures crawling over the sparkling sand.
Fun and laughter mirror the thoughts
Of happy families beside the sea.

George Oliver

THE GREY SEAL

As it slithered across the sand,
The waves broke in front of its eyes,
The seagulls circling overhead,
As the Grey Seal reached the sea.

It seemed to swim forever,
And as it reached its destination,
It climbed upon a rock and sat for a while,
It fell asleep and dreamt of far off waters.

It awoke and began to slither back across the rocks,
The waves broke in front of its eyes,
The seagulls circling overhead,
As the Grey Seal reached the sea.

And as it swam away it turned to say goodbye,
It seemed to swim forever,
And as it reached his home again,
The Grey Seal went to play.

Peter Parsons

DEATH

Death is where a man ticks your name off the list
of life.
He comes and puts a mask over your face and
Then you melt away like you'd never been there in
The first place. You're there in body but not in mind.
Your soul has left, he took it away, he throws it
in a cage with all the others. You tried to fight
Him off but to no avail. Death is the only
Certain thing that happens. It happens to us all
Because all our names are on the list of life. The
man will pay us a visit one day. He forces
The mask on top of your face, then he snatches
your
Spirit, it's just out of reach, thrown into a cage
You try to escape. You see your descendants, the
People before you. The people who made your life
In the first place. Now you're like them, just there in
memory.

Matthew Passmore

WHALEHUNT

The huge ship parts the ocean.
The whales scatter like panicked geese.
But there is no escape.
No escape from the flying harpoons,
That pierce like needles into a cushion,
That bite like the sharks that lurk in the sea.

The juggernaut creature writhes,
As salt spite enters the wound.
It spreads like venom through the body,
And struggling increases the pain.
But all too soon death arrives,
And the hunters cheer at their prize.

James Peach

REMEMBERING HISARONU

Through February's bleakness
I remember Hisaronu
where the sun shines
almost as brightly as its people's smiles.
I remember the villagers
who had so very little
yet gave so much to be our friends.
Our western culture had invaded their privacy,
built on their land,
but they had an acceptance of life's hardships
in a country where it's so difficult to succeed.
They bore no jealousy
believing our good fortune Allah's will
and shared with us fruit and nuts
without wanting anything in return
except our friendship.
I remember
the way we fascinated them,
how they complimented us
and made us believe it was we who were
beautiful.

Emma Phillips

THE CIRCUS

The lights seemed not as bright
When I last went to the circus
I saw the ladders up sequined tights
Of the aged and wrinkled acrobats.

But still the crowd clapped and cheered
Sightless to all indolent faults
Sightless to the horse's matted flanks
And sightless to the elephants twitch.

I couldn't help wondering
What went on inside their minds
Unaware of the elephants dank stench
Unaware of the fear in their eyes.

Not noticing how the elephant jangled its chain,
Not noticing the poodles pot bellies.
They just clapped and cheered to the crack of the whip
Unaware of the fear in their eyes.

Nicola Portus

GRIEVE DREAM

The sadness makes
the hurt
Scald.
Your past burns you still
Keeping you trapped
In your mourning.

Yet dawn comes.
The storm has gone
And the breeze returns.
Light.

Eleanor Pyart

ME

I am an artist
I am confident
Confident in my work, and my feelings.
I only paint the countryside,
Why?
It is healthy, fresh, colourful and quiet,
Not smokey, dull and noisy like the city.
I am free in the country.
Nobody here but me.
Me!

Donna Rainbow

RIVERS OF EMOTION

Our hearts ride
On rivers of emotion,
The river which flows
dangerously, swiftly.
Emotions have power,
power never seen,
power always felt.

A power unconquerable,
but still we learn
to supress it,
to harbour it,
to keep it inside.

But as a river floods
when strong rains come
when the water becomes too much to hold,
too much to be contained,
Emotions flood,
Overflow,
Pour out from within.

And when this tide comes,
when this wave breaks
with power unimaginable,
only a shell
of the former self is left.

Hannah Ruffles

DESTROYED MEMORIES

Sun-drenched beaches sit along the coast.
People wearing next to nothing
Flock to the beach
At the first sight
Of the summer sun.

Umbrellas form a multi-coloured sea,
Children run around screaming and splashing,
Dropping icecream on unsuspecting sunbathers,
While others brave the deceptive sewage-ridden waters.

Grandpa slouches, sleeping in his deckchair
With his "beer belly"
Sagging sadly over his trousers,
While Grandma sits eagerly knitting
A winter woolly for her favourite grandson.

But now it's all changed:
Oil chokes the stranded seagull
And discards it onshore.
Sewage pumps secretly out to sea,
While ashore, hyperdermic needles
Lie in wait
For the few people who risk a visit.

David Sapp

THE WOMAN AND THE WOMANIZER

The woman to the womanizer said,
"I see you winking wistfully at me
With your dark-green wicked eyes".
The womanizer smiled a winsome smile at the woman
And said
"Why woman. I warrant you
I wish you'd be my wife".
The woman said to the womanizer,
"You warped and wavering wangler,
I wish you wouldn't wink so wierdly,
It really gives me the willies".
"You're wrong you willful wisp.
Why be so wary of me?"
Said the womanizer to the woman.
The woman said to the womanizer,
"I see your wanton thoughts
And would you not wiggle your waist at me in that way".
"Don't whine,"
The womanizer said to the woman,
"I can see you weakening.
You wit is beginning to wane".
"I'm warning you,"
The woman wagged her finger at the womanizer.
"Don't try to weave your wicked web around me".
Then the womanizer said to the woman,
"Wendy! Wendy! It's me, William!
The window washer who gave you that ring
When you wept last Wednesday!"
And the woman said to the womanizer,
Oh William, you warm and wonderful man!
I wish you'd whisk me away".
Then the woman and the womanizer waltzed off wonkily
And warbled a wavering song.

Penny Sims

WINDOW

A shattered mosaic
A filter of sunlight
A ray of morning
A shadowless night

Laura Smith

GET TOGETHER

Playing gin-rummy
In a circle on the floor,
Eighteen thugs
And another two more.

Vincent Smith

MENTAL MELVIN

Mental Melvin
Made a mockery
Of mummy's macaroons.
Meany mummy
Gulped 'em down
With the aid of two wet spoons

Vincent Smith

THE SUMMER TREKKERS

In the heat of mid-July we would trek,
A collection of bare-legged children
And family dogs,
Passing through wide beams of yellow light,
Easing their way past towering leaves and branches,
Our summer shoes, once white, now brown,
As we disturbed the dry dust below.

A few more steps and the dirt became grass,
A startling array of colour
To be trampled and worn by our soiled shoes,
As we continued,
Down towards the river.

Here sunlight danced upon the gushing water -
The bed encrusted with diamonds,
And the sticklebacks darted
From one muddy bank to the other,
To the warm shadows,
Away from our prying eyes.

Louise Statt

DANCING SUNLIGHT

A pattern in flight,
It dances, flutters
Across the wall
Like water sparkling in the sun.
Drawn, I raise my head,
In a trance I stand,
Gazing out of the window.
My eyes explore the sky.
The legendary ball hanging,
The light of life,
With an unknown switch.

This flying ball,
Reaches out -
Long arms of light,
Grabbing.
Small fingers twist and turn,
Bending through the green jewels of the land.

They stand tall and strong,
Supported by miles of growing cable,
Tunnelled into the ground.
Their new summer clothes
Blow in the breeze.

These precious jewels,
dressed in summer clothes
Block out the light,
Send the fingers flying off
On another route.
Bending, they try again,
Stopped.
Will they win?
Is the flight too hard?

A gust of wind,
A breakthrough of light,
Long arms come reaching,
Searching,
Exploring.

They reach through the glass,
Turning,
They see.
A small child is playing.
With a magical power,
They pick her up,
Standing her by the window.

She gazes out,
The pattern of light,
Dances, Flutters
Across her face

Verity Sutcliffe

THE FOX AND THE HUNT

My home is a hole,
Though dark it be,
Surrounded by thousands of beautiful trees,
Wet leaves are dripping their dew on the ground,
And birds are singing contentedly.

The sound of branches moving with breeze,
In reality, no sound,
It's the silence that speaks.

I hear a noise as I stalk through the forest,
What was that?
What's going on?
Oh no, it's the hunt.

Then I run on and on,
Up hills so steep,
Across streams so wide,
And down valleys so deep.

Suddenly I feel my legs drop beneath me,
And before I know it I'm on the ground,
In a minute the hounds will tear me apart,
And my cubs shall die all alone.

Alison Wade

OLD AGE

On the park bench,
Sat an old man,
Walking stick by his side,
He sat all alone.

Ancient he looked,
With a face white as snow,
The moustache on his top lip,
Scruffy cap on his head,
The far off look in his blue eyes,
He looked almost dead.

People walked past him,
Past the old man, shaking their heads.

From his pocket,
He drew out some bread,
Munched on it thoughtfully,
Then sighed,
He remembered the old times,
When he was young and brisk.

The sun almost gone,
He got up to go,
Leaning on his old stick.

All that old man had left were his memories.

Geoffrey Walker

AUTUMN

As the face of summer turns away
Autumn takes her place.
Instead of lilac, pink and green
Warm tones are on her face.
Her cheeks are touched by a radiant glow,
With the softest hint of gold.
Joy she brings to children young,
Fond memories to the old.
She only stays 'til bonfire night,
The she must turn and go,
To make way as icy winter
Her seasonal face does show.

Luci Woodyatt

HIPPY'S ANTHEM

Hello, I'm an oak tree
I spread my branches
I don't like dead animals
I abide by the law of yin and yan
I love peace, man
I hate nuclear thingyummybobs
I dream among the stars
My roots are with the bracken
My mind is green based
Armageddan poses no threat to me
I use ozone friendly fly spray
I love nut cutlets
I'm losing my religion
I wear bells
I'm an oak and I wanna be a maple

Rosemary Worsley

A RELATIVE STRANGER

Scared, worried about meeting an old man,
his grandfather, a clock maker.
Remembering a cauldron,
with a hot bubbling mixture and
a faint smell of ammonia.
Dipping parts of watches and clocks
into it, to clean them.

A house in London,
a dark room, thick misty cigarette smoke.
Different, unlike his family home.
An insignificant thing, I think.
He was different. He didn't use ashtrays;
he tapped the burnt tobacco,
into his rolled up trousers.

He couldn't talk to him.
He dreaded visiting his Grandad.
When he got older,
he felt he could talk more
to try and get to know him.
But he left. He died,
a stranger to him.

Lizzie Wrigley